Y0-AGU-535

Tūtū Hamana

The Shaka Sign Story

Robert Lono ʻIkuwā
Nā Puke Hawaiʻi

Tūtū Hamana: The Shaka Sign Story
Copyright © 2007 Nā Puke Hawaiʻi

ISBN: 978-0-9798782-0-6

PRINTED IN CHINA

Photographers: Malia Andrus and Rena Thompson

Book designer: Rena Thompson

Archival pictures were provided by the Brigham Young University of Hawaiʻi Archives.

Proceeds benefit Hawaiian Language Education in Koʻolauloa, Oʻahu

www.napukehawaii.com

MAHALO NUI LOA

Rena Thompson
Malia Andrus
Kaʻimipono Teʻo-Tafiti
Kekela Miller
Ka ʻohana Teʻo-Tafiti
Matt Kester
Rebekah Kēhaulani Luke
Gladys Pualoa Ahuna
Amy Yamamoto
Masami Iida
Nā poʻe kūpuna o Lāʻie: yesterday, today, and tomorrow
BYU-Hawaiʻi Archives
Penmar Hawaiʻi

I love you all.
Lono ʻIkuwā

My *Tūtū* tells me all kinds of fascinating stories and songs. One evening, she sang me a funny, little tune about our fingers.

"Manamana lima,
Manamana lima...

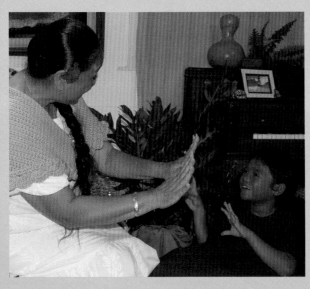

Nui, kuhi, waena,
Komo, iki,
Manamana lima..."

She said to me, "Ka'imi...what do we use our fingers for?" *Tūtū* always asks me about the *mana'o* of her songs. I smiled back and said...

"To rub...   to scratch...   to draw...

and to tickle!"

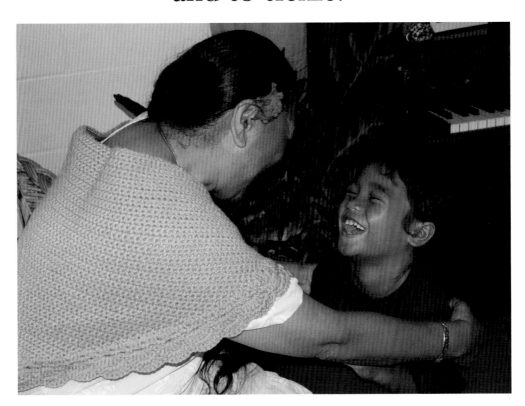

" 'Ā 'oia...Ka'imi. That's right. Now, what would happen if you never had your *manamana lima*? What would you do?"

That was a tough question...so I paused and thought...then said quietly, "I don't know *Tūtū*."

She smiled back
and responded, " *ʻAʻole
pilikia*...no problem
Kaʻimi. *Tūtū* is going
to tell you a story about
one of our *Kupuna*.
    His name was
Hamana Kalili."

Tūtū Hamana was a great and famous fisherman in *Koʻolauloa*...from *Kaʻaʻwa* all the way to *Waimea*. The people of *Lāʻie* loved him because he was a giving and caring man.

As a little girl, I
thought he was
a very strong
and hard worker.
That was true.

In fact, one day while he was working at the sugar plantation, something really unfortunate happened.

His three middle fingers were chopped off in an accident.

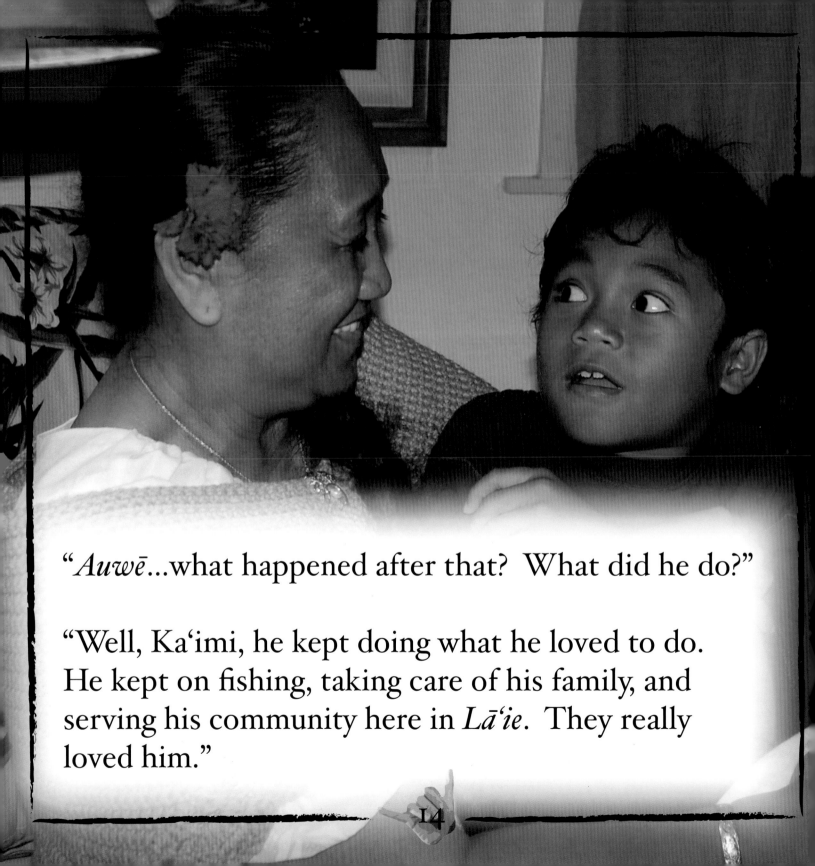

"*Auwē*...what happened after that? What did he do?"

"Well, Ka'imi, he kept doing what he loved to do. He kept on fishing, taking care of his family, and serving his community here in *Lā'ie*. They really loved him."

*"Maikaʻi kēlā moʻolelo, Tūtū...*that's a nice story"
said Kaʻimi.

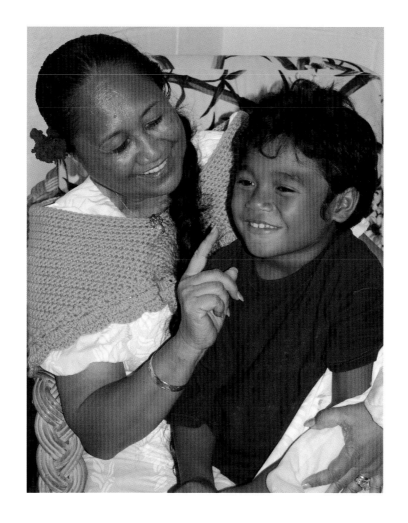

"Tūtū replied quickly, *" ʻAʻole i pau...*it's not finished yet."

On another day, some of the community men were fixing the Church building here in *Lāʻie*, and you will not guess what happened...

but the Church accidentally caught on fire and was completely destroyed.

The people of *Lāʻie* pulled together and stayed strong. They prayed and fasted to their Heavenly Father for his help and guidance.

So...after discussing what they should do, the community decided to hold a *hukilau* to raise money to build another Church.

(Tūtū Hamana is in the center crossing hands.)

"What's a *hukilau*?" asked Ka'imi.

"Oh...the *hukilau!!!*" *Tūtū* began to sing...

Oh we're going to a hukilau, a huki, hukilau... Everybody loves the hukilau...

Those were wonderful days. Our people worked together and had all kinds of activities for the *malihini*.

We danced...

We sang...

We made all kinds of food: *poi*, *lomi* salmon, chicken long rice, and *kalua* pig.

And my favorite...

was doing the *hukilau*...oh yes, the *hukilau*. Everyone would gather together at the beach and pull the rope. And you know, Ka'imi, *Tūtū* Hamana was the head fisherman of the *hukilau*.

He would yell out with his thunderous voice, *"Huki ke kaula, huki ke kaula...huki, huki mai..."* We would pull the rope and catch a bunch of fish.

HAWAIIAN HUKILAU OR NET FISHING

And then...we would serve the guests their food and put on a show for them.

Tūtū Hanama was even the great *ali'i* in the court. He was a man full of *aloha* and kindness. We loved him so much, and so did our *malihini*.

It was funny how it all happened, but when the guests would leave, *Tūtū* Hamana would wave goodbye to them with his old, beat up hand. And the people out of great *aloha*, would wave back to him with their three middle fingers down like the shaka sign.

Ka'imi, that's how we got the shaka sign here in Hawai'i...from our great, old *Tūtū* Hamana.

Can you believe that? Don't forget, honey boy, that when life gets tough or when something unfortunate happens to you...please, please don't forget *Tūtū* Hamana and shaka to everyone you see.

Glossary

Ali'i: Chief

'A'ole: No; not

'Ā 'oia: Right on!

'A'ole pilikia: no problem

Huki: pull

Iki: pinky (finger)

Kaula: rope

Kēlā: that

Komo: ring (finger)

Kuhi: pointer (finger)

Kupuna: ancestor

Maika'i: good

Malihini: guest; visitor

Manamana lima: fingers

Mana'o: thought; meaning

Mo'olelo: story

Nui: thumb (finger)

Pau: done

Tūtū: grandparent

Waena: middle (finger)

Robert Lono ʻIkuwā, a native of Kalaoa, Kona finds unparallel content in backyard discussions and overnight talk story sessions. As an unlearned polyglot, he esteems the essence of Language as a major contributor to the shaping and molding of an individual's identity. Moreover, with the extreme commercialization and glamorization of Hawaiian folklore and culture, Mr. ʻIkuwā fulfills the lack of needed indigenous literature for both young and old.

Mr. ʻIkuwā acquired a multi-cultural education from both western and indigenous institutions. Mr. ʻIkuwā received a bachelor degree in international cultural communications and a master degree in public administration from Brigham Young University; respectively from Hawaiʻi and Utah.

In the indigenous realm, Mr. ʻIkuwā has been endowed as Kumu Hula and prizes his scholarship as a Hawaiian language speaker from the Kūpuna of Nā Kona. As a Hawaiian language instructor for the past ten years, Mr. ʻIkuwā believes storytelling in our native tongue must flourish in both informal and formal settings. This book project is a mere attempt in that direction.